Conflict

Themes

a Teacher's Book accompanies each volume

Also edited by Rhodri Jones

an introductory series

Preludes

one Teacher's Book covers the whole series

Conflict

edited by Rhodri Jones

Heinemann Educational Books
London

Heinemann Educational Books Ltd
LONDON EDINBURGH MELBOURNE AUCKLAND TORONTO
SINGAPORE HONG KONG KUALA LUMPUR
IBADAN NAIROBI JOHANNESBURG
LUSAKA NEW DELHI

ISBN 0 435 14482 0

Published by Heinemann Educational Books Ltd
48 Charles Street, London W1X 8AH
Printed Offset Litho and bound in Great Britain by
Cox & Wyman Ltd, London, Fakenham and Reading

Acknowledgements

The Editor and Publisher wish to thank the following for permission to reprint copyright material: Faber & Faber Ltd for 'Child on Top of a Greenhouse' by Theodore Roethke from *Collected Poems;* R. N. Currey for 'Lesson in Murder'; James Stephens and Macmillan & Co Ltd for 'Shame' from *Collected Poems;* Raymond Souster and The Ryerson Press for 'The Man who finds that his Son has become a Thief' from *The Colour of the Times;* Tony Connor and Oxford University Press for 'The Burglary' from *With Love Somehow;* William Plomer and Jonathan Cape Ltd for 'Move On' from *Collected Poems;* permission to include 'The Laws of God, the Laws of Man' and 'Oh who is that young Sinner' has been granted by the Society of Authors as the literary representative of the Estate of A. E. Housman, and Jonathan Cape Ltd, publishers of A. E. Housman's *Collected Poems;* Carl Sandburg and Harcourt, Brace & World Inc for 'A Teamster's Farewell' from *Chicago Poems;* Stevie Smith and Longmans Green & Co Ltd for 'The Commuted Sentence' from *Harold's Leap;* Putnam & Co Ltd and John Pudney for 'This Malefactor' from *Collected Poems;* 'The Hang Man at Home' from *Smoke and Steel* by Carl Sandburg, copyright 1920 by Harcourt, Brace & World Inc, renewed 1948 by Carl Sandburg, reprinted by permission of the publishers; Ralph Hodgson and Macmillan & Co Ltd for 'To Hang a Man' from *The Skylark;* Mary Gilmore and Angus & Robertson Ltd for part of 'The Disinherited' from *Selected Verse;* Laurence Lerner and The Hogarth Press for 'What's the Difference' from *The Directions of Memory;* Philip Hobsbaum and Messrs Macmillan for 'The Place's Fault'; Stephen Spender and Faber & Faber Ltd for 'My Parents kept me from Children who were Rough' from *Collected Poems;* Dannie Abse and Hutchinson & Co Ltd for 'Red Balloon' from *Poems, Golders Green;* R. S. Thomas and Rupert Hart-Davis Ltd for 'Strangers' and 'Tramp' from *The Bread of Truth;* The Trustees for the copyrights of the late Dylan Thomas and J. M. Dent & Sons Ltd for 'The Hunchbank in the Park' from *Collected Poems;* Sally Roberts and J. M. Dent & Sons Ltd for 'A Small Tragedy' from *Welsh Voices;* 'Counting the Mad', copyright 1957 by Donald Justice, reprinted from *The Summer Anniversaries* by Donald Justice by permission of Wesleyan University Press; Andrew Young and Rupert Hart-Davis Ltd for 'The White Blackbird' from *Collected Poems;* D. J. Enright and Chatto & Windus for 'In the Catalogue' and 'Mr Weary's Room' from *The Old Adam;* Robert

Morgan and Rupert Hart-Davis Ltd for 'Tramps on Waterloo Station' and 'Maladjusted Boys'; John Pudney and Putnam & Co Ltd for 'Lines Written on the A20 Arterial Road'; Herbert Read and Faber & Faber Ltd for 'The Refugees' from *Collected Poems;* W. H. Auden and Faber & Faber Ltd for 'Say this city has ten million souls', 'Let me tell you a little story'; Louis Simpson and Oxford University Press for 'The Boarder' from *Selected Poems;* Alan Brownjohn and The Digby Press for 'In This City' from *The Railings;* Philip Larkin and Faber & Faber Ltd for 'Mr Bleaney' from *Whitsun Weddings;* Martin Seymour-Smith and Abelard Schuman Ltd for 'Found on a Building Site' from *Tea with Miss Stockport;* Stevie Smith and Andre Deutsch Ltd for 'Not Waving but Drowning' from *Not Waving but Drowning;* John Hall and Chatto & Windus Ltd for 'Suicides' from *The Burning Hare;* Bernard Spencer and Alan Ross Ltd for 'Train to Work' and 'Cage' from *Collected Poems;* George Jonas for 'For the record'; Michael Hamburger and Longmans Green & Co Ltd for 'Security' from *Weather and Season;* Roy Daniels and McClelland & Stewart Ltd for 'Noah'; Jiri Filip and Hutchinson & Co Ltd for 'The Fable of the Trained White Horse' from *Back to Life;* Faber & Faber Ltd for 'The State' by Randall Jarrell from *Selected Poems;* Mieczyslaw Jastrun and Hutchinson & Co Ltd for 'The Epoch' from *Back to Life;* Ann Elmo Agency Inc for 'Song of the Storm Trooper'; Ted Hughes and Faber & Faber Ltd for 'Bayonet Charge' from *The Hawk in the Rain;* George Sassoon and Faber & Faber Ltd for 'Memorial Tablet' and 'Lamentations' from *Collected Poems;* Mr Harold Owen and Chatto & Windus Ltd for 'Dulce et Decorum Est' from *The Collected Poems of Wilfred Owen;* Martin Bell and Penguin Books Ltd for 'Reason for Refusal' from *Penguin Modern Poets 3;* Karl Shapiro and Random House Inc for 'The Conscientious Objector'; James Michie and Rupert Hart-Davis Ltd for 'Dooley is a Traitor' from *Possible Laughter;* James Kirkup and Oxford University Press for 'Undivided Loyalty' and 'No more Hiroshimas' from *Refusal to Conform;* Susan Gowers for 'The Temptation'; Barrie Law for 'The Boy Who lives down our Street'; Jemal Isfendiyar for 'When I walk in the Market Square'; the Headmaster of Lampton School, Hounslow, for 'Last Lesson of the Afternoon' by Susan Ford; Linda Whitehead for 'The Row'. Mrs George Bambridge' and Macmillan & Co Ltd for 'Cells' from *The Collected Poems of Rudyard Kipling;* Joseph Kariuki for 'Come Away my Love'; R. A. K. Mason for 'On the Swag'; Laurence Pollinger Ltd, the Estate of the late Mrs Freida Lawrence and William Heinemann Ltd for 'Last Lesson of the Afternoon' from *The Complete Poems of D. H. Lawrence;* the Executors of the Estate of A. S. J. Tessimond for 'The Man in the Bowler Hat' from *Voices in a Giant City.*

Contents

Conforming and Protesting

Crime and Punishment

An eighteenth-century highwayman at the gallows. By courtesy of the Mansell Collection.

Child on Top of a Greenhouse

Theodore Roethke

The wind billowing out the seat of my britches,
My feet crackling splinters of glass and dried putty,
The half-grown chrysanthemums staring up like accusers,
Up through the streaked glass, flashing with sunlight,
A few white clouds all rushing eastward,
A line of elms plunging and tossing like horses,
And everyone, everyone pointing up and shouting!

The Temptation

Susan Gowers (aged 14)

I was walking slowly along the road.
It was quiet and dark.
All I could see were old houses,
Empty houses,
Not a window broken.
They look so tempting,
I just can't resist it.
I pick up a stone,
And crash!
The whole street is awake.
They're all looking at me.
There are faces everywhere.
I'm getting scared.
I don't know which way to turn.
Then I run straight down the hill
As fast as I can.
They're all pushing me away.

Lesson in Murder

R. N. Currey

I drew the smooth round pebble back;
   I felt the strong release;
I did not know that thud would crack
   The thin bones of my peace.

The jewelled bird fell from the tree,
  Half-fluttered to my feet;
The others snatched it up to see
  If any warm pulse beat.

They filled the leafy air with cries,
  Re-lived the redstart thrill,
Ruffled a rainbow in my eyes;
  While I stood sick and still –

And, head averted, bent and took
  Another five smooth stones,
With catapult fingers cocked a snook
  At aching greenstick bones.

Shame

James Stephens

I was ashamed! I dared not lift my eyes!
I could not bear to look upon the skies!
What I had done! Sure, everybody knew!
From everywhere hands pointed where I stood,
And scornful eyes were piercing through and through
The moody armour of my hardihood!

I heard their voices too, each word an asp
That buzz'd and stung me sudden as a flame!
And all the world was jolting on my name!
And now and then there came a wicked rasp
Of laughter, jarring me to deeper shame!

And then I looked, and there was no one nigh!
No eyes that stabbed like swords or glinted sly!
No laughter creaking on the silent air!
– And then I saw that I was all alone
Facing my soul! And next I was aware
That this mad mockery was all my own!

4

The Man who finds that his Son has become a Thief

Raymond Souster

Coming into the store at first angry
As the accusation, believing in
The word of his boy who has told him:
I didn't steal anything, honest.

Then coming calmer, seeing that anger
Will not help in the business, listening painfully
As the other's evidence unfolds, so painfully slow.

Then seeing gradually that evidence
Almost as if tighten slowly around the neck
Of his son, at first vaguely circumstantial, then gathering damage,
Until there is present the unmistakable odour of guilt
Which seeps now into the mind and lays its poison.

Suddenly feeling sick and alone and afraid,
As if an unseen hand had slapped him in the face
For no reason whatsoever: wanting to get out
Into the street, the night, the darkness, anywhere to hide
The pain that must show in the face to these strangers, the fear.

It must be like this.
It could hardly be otherwise.

I know some lonely Houses

Emily Dickinson

I know some lonely houses off the road
A robber'd like the look of –
Wooden barred,
And windows hanging low,
Inviting to
A portico,

Where two could creep:
One hand the tools,
The other peep
To make sure all's asleep.
Old-fashioned eyes,
Not easy to surprise!

How orderly the kitchen'd look by night,
With just a clock —
But they could gag the tick,
And mice won't bark;
And so the walls don't tell,
None will.

A pair of spectacles ajar just stir —
An almanac's aware.
Was it the mat winked,
Or a nervous star?
The moon slides down the stair
To see who's there.

There's plunder — where?
Tankard, or spoon,
Earring, or stone,
A watch, some ancient brooch
To match the grandmamma,
Staid sleeping there.

Dry rattles, too,
Stealth's slow;
The sun has got as far
As the third sycamore.
Screams chanticleer,
'Who's there?'

And echoes, trains away,
Sneer — 'Where?'
While the old couple, just astir,
Think that the sunrise left the door ajar!

The Burglary

Tony Connor

It's two o'clock now; somebody's pausing in the street
to turn up his collar. The night's black: distraught
with chimney-toppling wind and harsh rain —
see, the wet's soaking in on the end-gable,
and the frothing torrent, overspilling the broken drain,

6

accosts the pavement with incoherent babble.
There is the house we want: how easy to burgle,
with its dark trees, and the lawn set back from the road;
the owners will be in bed now – the old couple;
you've got the position of the safe? – Yes, I know the code.

The cock's going mad up there on the church steeple;
the wind's enormous – will it ever stifle;
still, its noise, and the rain's are with us, I daresay,
they'll cover what we make, if we go careful
round by the greenhouse, and in at the back way.

Here's the broken sash I mentioned; – no need to be fearful,
watch how I do it: these fingers are facile
with the practice I've had on worse nights than this.
I tell you, the whole thing's going to be a doddle:
the way I've got it worked out, we can't miss.

Although, God knows, most things turn out a muddle,
and it only confuses more to look for a moral.
Wherever I've been the wind and rain's blown; –
I've done my best to hang on, as they tried to whittle
the name from the action, the flesh away from the bone,

but I think, sometimes, I'm fighting a losing battle.
So many bad nights; so many strange houses to burgle;
and every job done with a mate I don't know: –
oh, you're all right; I don't mean to be personal,
but when the day breaks, you'll have your orders, and go.

Then, the next time the foul weather howls in the ginnel;
when the slates slide, the brimming gutters gurgle;
there'll be another lad I've never seen before,
with the rest of the knowledge that makes the job possible
as I ease up a window or skeleton-key a door.

Still, it's my only life, and I've no quarrel
with the boss's methods; – apart from the odd quibble
about allowances and fair rates of pay,
or the difficult routes I often have to travel,
or the fact that I never get a holiday.

Most of the time, though, I'm glad of mere survival,
even at the stormiest hour of the darkest vigil.
. . . Here's the hall door; under the stairs you said?
This one's easy, because the old folk are feeble,
and lie in their curtained room, sleeping like the dead.

Sometimes, believe me, it's a lot more trouble,
when you've got to be silent, and move as though through
 treacle.
Now hold your breath while I let these tumblers click . . .
I've done these many a time . . . a well known model;
one more turn now . . . Yes; that does the trick.

Nothing inside? The same recurrent muddle;
I think the most careful plan's a bloody marvel
if it plays you true, if nothing at all goes wrong.
Well, let's be off; we've another place to tackle
under the blown, black rain; and the dawn won't be long

when the wind will drop, and the rain become a drizzle,
and you'll go your way. Leaving me the bedraggled
remnants of night, that walk within the head
long after the sun-shot gutters cease to trickle,
and I draw my curtains, and topple into bed.

Move On

William Plomer

They made love under bridges, lacking beds,
And engines whistled them a bridal song,
A sudden bull's-eye showed them touching heads,
Policemen told them they were doing wrong;
And when they slept on seats in public gardens
Told them, 'Commit no nuisance in the park';
The beggars, begging the policemen's pardons,
Said that they thought as it was after dark –

At this the law grew angry and declared
Outlaws who outrage by-laws are the devil;
At this the lovers only stood and stared,
As well they might, for they had meant no evil;
'Move on,' the law said. To avoid a scene
They moved. And thus we keep our cities clean.

Oh who is that young Sinner?

A. E. Housman

Oh who is that young sinner with the handcuffs on his wrists?
And what has he been after that they groan and shake their fists?
And wherefore is he wearing such a conscience-stricken air?
Oh they're taking him to prison for the colour of his hair.

'Tis a shame to human nature, such a head of hair as his;
In the good old time 'twas hanging for the colour that it is;
Though hanging isn't bad enough and flaying would be fair
For the nameless and abominable colour of his hair.

Oh a deal of pains he's taken and a pretty price he's paid
To hide his poll or dye it of a mentionable shade;
But they've pulled the beggar's hat off for the world to see and
    stare,
And they're taking him to justice for the colour of his hair.

Now 'tis oakum for his fingers and the treadmill for his feet,
And the quarry-gang on Portland in the cold and in the heat,
And between his spells of labour in the time he has to spare
He can curse the God that made him for the colour of his hair.

The Laws of God, the Laws of Man

A. E. Housman

    The laws of God, the laws of man,
He may keep that will and can;
Not I: let God and man decree
Laws for themselves and not for me;
And if my ways are not as theirs
Let them mind their own affairs.
Their deeds I judge and much condemn,
Yet when did I make laws for them?
Please yourselves, say I, and they
Need only look the other way.
But no, they will not; they must still
Wrest their neighbour to their will,
And make me dance as they desire
With jail and gallows and hell-fire.

And how am I to face the odds
Of man's bedevilment and God's?
I, a stranger and afraid
In a world I never made.
They will be master, right or wrong;
Though both are foolish, both are strong
And since, my soul, we cannot fly
To Saturn nor to Mercury,
Keep we must if we can,
These foreign laws of God and man.

A Small Tragedy

Sally Roberts

They came up in the evening
And said to him, 'Fly!
All is discovered!'
And he fled.

A quiet little man,
Of no importance.
In fifty years he had acquired
Only flat feet and spectacles
And a distressing cough.

After a month or more,
(He having gone so quickly)
An inspector called
And they began to find the bodies.

A large number of them,
Stuffed into cupboards and other corners.
(At work he was tidy,
But files and paper-clips
Are matters of some importance.)

In the end, of course,
He was hanged,
Very neatly,
Though pleading insanity.

A quiet little man,
Who knew what to do with files and paper-clips
But had no ideas about people
Except to destroy them.

Jim Jones

Anon

O, listen for a moment lads, and hear me tell my tale –
How, o'er the sea from England's shore I was compelled to sail.
The jury says, 'He's guilty, sir,' and says the judge, says he –
'For life, Jim Jones, I'm sending you across the stormy sea;
And take my tip before you ship to join the iron-gang,
Don't be too gay at Botany Bay, or else you'll surely hang –
Or else you'll hang,' he says, says he – 'and after that, Jim Jones,
High up upon the gallow-tree the crows will pick your bones –
You'll have no chance for mischief then; remember what I say,
They'll flog the poaching out of you, out there at Botany Bay.'

The winds blew hard upon the sea, and the pirates came along,
But the soldiers on our convict ship were full five hundred strong,
They opened fire and somehow drove that pirate ship away.
I'd have rather joined that pirate ship than come to Botany Bay:
For night and day the irons clang, and like poor galley slaves
We toil, and toil, and when we die must fill dishonoured graves.
But by and by I'll break my chains: into the bush I'll go,
And join the brave bushrangers there – Jack Donohoo and Co.;
And some dark night when everything is silent in the town
I'll kill the tyrants, one and all, and shoot the floggers down:
I'll give the Law a little shock: remember what I say,
They'll yet regret they sent Jim Jones in chains to Botany Bay.

The Wild Colonial Boy

Anon

'Tis of a wild Colonial boy, Jack Doolan was his name,
Of poor but honest parents he was born in Castlemaine.
He was his father's only hope, his mother's only joy,
And dearly did his parents love the wild Colonial boy.

Chorus:
Come, all my hearties, we'll roam the mountains high,
Together we will plunder, together we will die.
We'll wander over valleys, and gallop over plains,
And we'll scorn to live in slavery, bound down with iron chains.

He was scarcely sixteen years of age when he left his father's
     home,
And through Australia's sunny clime a bushranger did roam,
He robbed those wealthy squatters, their stock he did destroy,
And a terror to Australia was the wild Colonial boy.

In sixty-one this daring youth commenced his wild career,
With a heart that knew no danger, no foeman did he fear.
He stuck up the Beechworth mail-coach, and robbed Judge
     MacEvoy,
Who trembled, and gave up his gold to the wild Colonial boy.

He bade the judge 'Good morning', and told him to beware,
That he'd never rob a hearty chap that acted on the square,
And never to rob a mother of her son and only joy,
Or else you may turn outlaw, like the wild Colonial boy.

One day as he was riding the mountain-side along,
A-listening to the little birds, their pleasant laughing song,
Three mounted troopers rode alone – Kelly, Davis, and FitzRoy –
They thought that they would capture him, the wild Colonial boy.

'Surrender now, Jack Doolan, you see there's three to one.
Surrender now, Jack Doolan, you daring highwayman.'
He drew a pistol from his belt, and shook the little toy.
'I'll fight, but not surrender,' said the wild Colonial boy.

He fired at Trooper Kelly and brought him to the ground,
And in return from Davis received a mortal wound.
All shattered through the jaws he lay still firing at FitzRoy,
And that's the way they captured him – the wild Colonial boy.

The Death of Ben Hall

Anon

Ben Hall was out on the Lachlan side
With a thousand pounds on his head;
A score of troopers were scattered wide
And a hundred more were ready to ride
Wherever a rumour led.

They had followed his track from the Weddin heights
And north by the Weelong yards;
Through dazzling days and moonlit nights
They had sought him over the rifle-sights,
With their hands on their trigger-guards.

The outlaw stole like a hunted fox
Through the scrub and stunted heath,
And peered like a hawk from his eyrie rocks
Through the waving boughs of the sapling box
On the troopers riding beneath.

His clothes were rent by the clutching thorn
And his blistered feet were bare;
Ragged and torn, with his beard unshorn,
He hid in the woods like a beast forlorn,
With a padded path to his lair.

But every night when the white stars rose
He crossed by the Gunning Plain
To a stockman's hut where the Gunning flows,
And struck on the door three swift light blows,
And a hand unhooked the chain –

And the outlaw followed the lone path back
With food for another day;
And the kindly darkness covered his track
And the shadows swallowed him deep and black
Where the starlight melted away.

But his friend had read of the Big Reward,
And his soul was stirred with greed;
He fastened his door and window-board,
He saddled his horse and crossed the ford,
And spurred to the town at speed.

You may ride at a man's or a maid's behest
When honour or true love call
And steel your heart to the worst or best,
But the ride that is ta'en on a traitor's quest
Is the bitterest ride of all.

A hot wind blew from the Lachlan bank
And a curse on its shoulder came;
The pine trees frowned at him, rank on rank,
The sun on a gathering storm-cloud sank
And flushed his cheek with shame.

He reined at the Court; and the tale began
That the rifles alone should end;
Sergeant and trooper laid their plan
To draw the net on the hunted man
At the treacherous word of a friend.

False was the hand that raised the chain
And false was the whispered word:
'The troopers have turned to the south again,
You may dare to camp on the Gunning Plain.'
And the weary outlaw heard.

He walked from the hut but a quarter-mile
Where a clump of saplings stood
In a sea of grass like a lonely isle;
And the moon came up in a little while
Like silver steeped in blood.

Ben Hall lay down on the dew-wet ground
By the side of his tiny fire;
And a night-breeze woke, and he heard no sound
As the troopers drew their cordon round —
And the traitor earned his hire.

And nothing they saw in the dim grey light,
But the little glow in the trees;
And they crouched in the tall cold grass all night,
Each one ready to shoot at sight,
With his rifle cocked on his knees.

When the shadows broke and the dawn's white sword
Swung over the mountain wall,
And a little wind blew over the ford,
A sergeant sprang to his feet and roared:
'In the name of the Queen, Ben Hall!'

Haggard, the outlaw leapt from his bed
With his lean arms held on high.
'Fire!' And the word was scarcely said
When the mountains rang to a rain of lead —
And the dawn went drifting by.

They kept their word and they paid his pay
Where a clean man's hand would shrink;
And that was the traitor's master-day
As he stood by the bar on his homeward way
And called on the crowd to drink.

He banned no creed and he barred no class,
And he called to his friends by name;
But the worst would shake his head and pass
And none would drink from the bloodstained glass
And the goblet red with shame.

And I know when I heard the last grim call
And my mortal hour is spent,
When the light is hid and the curtains fall
I would rather sleep with the dead Ben Hall
Than go where that traitor went.

Feare

Robert Herrick

Man must do well out of a good intent;
Not for the servile feare of punishment.

A Teamster's Farewell

Carl Sandburg

Sobs En Route to a Penitentiary

Good-bye now to the streets and the clash of wheels and locking
    hubs,
The sun coming on the brass buckles and harness knobs,
The muscles of the horses sliding under their heavy haunches,
Good-bye now to the traffic policeman and his whistle,
The smash of the iron hoof on the stones,
All the crazy wonderful slamming roar of the street —
O God, there's noises I'm going to be hungry for.

Dungeon

Samuel Taylor Coleridge

And this place our forefathers made for man!
This is the process of our love and wisdom,
To each poor brother who offends against us –
Most innocent, perhaps – and what if guilty?
Is this the only cure? Merciful God!
Each pore and natural outlet shrivell'd up
By Ignorance and parching Poverty,
His energies roll back upon his heart,
And stagnate and corrupt; till chang'd to poison,
They break out on him, like a loathsome plague-spot;
Then we call in our pamper'd mountebanks –
And this is their best cure! uncomforted
And friendless solitude, groaning and tears,
And savage faces, at the clanking hour,
Seen through the steams and vapour of this dungeon,
By the lamp's dismal twilight! So he lies
Circled with evil, till his very soul
Unmoulds its essence, hopelessly deform'd
By sights of ever more deformity!

With other ministrations thou, O Nature!
Healest thy wandering and distemper'd child:
Thou pourest on him thy soft influences,
Thy sunny hues, fair forms, and breathing sweets,
Thy melodies of woods, and winds, and waters,
Till he relent, and can no more endure
To be a jarring and a dissonant thing,
Amid this general dance and minstrelsy;
But, bursting into tears, wins back his way,
His angry spirit heal'd and harmoniz'd
By the benignant touch of Love and Beauty

The Commuted Sentence

Stevie Smith

Shut me not alive away
From the light of every day
Hang me rather by the neck to die
Against a morning sky.

Oh shut me not behind a prison wall
I have a horror of this sort of place
Where I may sit and count the hours pass
And never see a smiling human face.

Here is all straight and narrow as a tomb
Oh shut me not within a little room.

Cells

Rudyard Kipling

I've a head like a concertina, I've a tongue like a button-stick,
I've a mouth like an old potato, and I'm more than a little sick,
But I've had my fun o' the Corp'ral's Guard; I've made the cinders
   fly,
And I'm here in the Clink for a thundering drink and blacking the
   Corporal's eye.

> With a second-hand overcoat under my head,
>   And a beautiful view of the yard,
> O it's pack-drill for me and a fortnight's C.B.
>   For 'drunk and resisting the Guard!'
>   Mad drunk and resisting the Guard –
>   'Strewth, but I socked it them hard!
> So it's pack-drill for me and a fortnight's C.B
>   For 'drunk and resisting the Guard.'

I started o' canteen porter, I finished o' canteen beer,
But a dose o' gin that a mate slipped in, it was that that brought
   me here.
'Twas that and an extry double Guard that rubbed my nose in the
   dirt –
But I fell away with the Corp'ral's stock and the best of the
   Corp'ral's shirt.

I left my cap in a public-house, my boots in the public road,
And Lord knows where – and I don't care – my belt and my tunic
   goed.
They'll stop my pay, they'll cut away the stripes I used to wear,
But I left my mark on the Corp'ral's face, and I think he'll keep it
   there!

My wife she cries on the barrack-gate, my kid in the barrack-yard.
It ain't that I mind the Ord'ly room – it's *that* that cuts so hard.
I'll take my oath before them both that I will sure abstain,
But as soon as I'm in with a mate and gin, I know I'll do it again!

With a second-hand overcoat under my head,
And a beautiful view of the yard,
Yes, it's pack-drill for me and a fortnight's C.B.
For 'drunk and resisting the Guard!'
Mad drunk and resisting the Guard –
'Strewth, but I socked it them hard!
So it's pack-drill for me and a fortnight's C.B.
For 'drunk and resisting the Guard.'

Bird in a Cage

Anon

Bird in a cage, love,
Bird in a cage,
Waiting for Willie
To come back to me.

Roses are red, love,
Violets are blue.
God in heaven
Knows I love you.

Write me a letter,
Write it today.
Stamp it tomorrow,
Send it away.

Write me a letter,
Send it by mail.
Send and direct it
To Lexington jail.

Bird in a cage, love,
Bird in a cage,
Waiting for Willie
To come back to me.

Clever Tom Clinch going to be Hanged

Jonathan Swift

As clever *Tom Clinch*, while the Rabble was bawling,
Rode stately through *Holbourn*, to die in his Calling;
He stopt at the *George* for a Bottle of Sack,
And promis'd to pay for it when he'd come back.
His Waistcoat and Stockings, and Breeches were white,
His Cap had a new Cherry Ribbon to ty't.
The Maids to the Doors and the Balconies ran,
And said, lack-a-day! he's a proper young Man.
But, as from the Windows the Ladies he spy'd,
Like a Beau in the Box, he bow'd low on each Side;
And when his last Speech the loud Hawkers did cry,
He swore from his Cart, it was all a damn'd Lye.
And when his last Speech the loud Hawkers did cry,
The Hangman for Pardon fell down on his Knee;
Tom gave him a Kick in the Guts for his Fee.
Then said, I must speak to the People a little,
But I'll see you all damn'd before I will *whittle*.
My honest Friend *Wild*, may he long hold his Place,
He lengthen'd my Life with a whole Year of Grace.
Take Courage, dear Comrades, and be not afraid,
Nor slip this Occasion to follow your Trade.
My Conscience is clear, and my Spirits are calm,
And thus I go off without Pray'r-Book or Psalm.
Then follow the Practice of clever *Tom Clinch*,
Who hung like a Hero, and never would flinch.

whittle = A word for confessing at the Gallows.

A London Fête

Coventry Patmore

All night fell hammers, shock on shock;
With echoes Newgate's granite clanged:
The scaffold built, at eight o'clock
They brought the man out to be hanged.
Then came from all the people there
A single cry, that shook the air;
Mothers held up their babies to see,

Who spread their hands, and crowed with glee;
Here a girl from her vesture tore
A rag to wave with, and joined the roar;
There a man, with yelling tired,
Stopped, and the culprit's crime inquired;
A sot, below the doomed man dumb,
Bawled his health in the world to come;
These blasphemed and fought for places;
These, half-crushed, with frantic faces,
To windows, where, in freedom sweet,
Others enjoyed the wicked treat.
At last, the show's black crisis pended;
Struggles for better standings ended;
The rabble's lips no longer cursed,
But stood agape with horrid thirst;
Thousands of breasts beat horrid hope;
Thousands of eyeballs, lit with hell,
Burnt one way all, to see the rope
Unslacken as the platform fell.
The rope flew tight; and then the roar
Burst forth afresh; less loud, but more
Confused and affrighting than before.
A few harsh tongues for ever led
The common din, the chaos of noises,
But ear could not catch what they said.
As when the realm of the damned rejoices
At winning a soul to its will,
That clatter and clangour of hateful voices
Sickened and stunned the air, until
The dangling corpse hung straight and still.
The show complete, the pleasure past,
The solid masses loosened fast;
A thief slunk off, with ample spoil,
To ply elsewhere his daily toil;
A baby strung its doll to a stick;
A mother praised the pretty trick;
Two children caught and hanged a cat;
Two friends walked on, in lively chat;
And two, who had disputed places,
Went forth to fight, with murderous faces.

This Malefactor

John Pudney

This malefactor dies how many times a day,
With warders in fair play
With dominoes or rummy, draughts or whist.
Let's hope they give the rope the proper twist!

The brute who killed for passion, or for greed,
Now waits a colder deed,
Precisely done by one who is expert.
For Christ's sake is it easy, will it hurt?

This malefactor dies how many times a night,
Within a warder's sight.
And cons the details as he dreams and wakes.
What happens if this bloody rope-length breaks?

This brute, who killed but once, dies now again,
And often, without pain,
Until his neck is broken, dead on time.
Is it a fact they chuck you in quick-lime?

God give you Sunday patience till you die
Beneath a Tuesday sky!
May God have special mercy to endow!
God, in your mercy, can't you make it now?

The Hang Man at Home

Carl Sandburg

What does the hangman think about
When he goes home at night from work?
When he sits down with his wife and
Children for a cup of coffee and a
Plate of ham and eggs, do they ask
Him if it was a good day's work
And everything went well or do they
Stay off such topics and talk about
The weather, baseball, politics
And the comic strips in the papers
And the movies? Do they look at his
Hands when he reaches for the coffee

Or the ham and eggs? If the little
Ones say, Daddy, play horse, here's
A rope – does he answer like a joke:
I seen enough rope for today?
Or does his face light up like a
Bonfire of joy and does he say:
It's a good and dandy world we live
In. And if a white face moon looks
In through a window where a baby girl
Sleeps and the moon gleams mix with
Baby ears and baby hair– the hangman –
How does he act then? It must be easy
For him. Anything is easy for a hangman,
I guess.

To Hang a Man

Ralph Hodgson

To hang a man:
To fit the cap,
And fix the rope,
And slide the bar,
And let him drop.
I know, I know:
What can you do!
You have no choice,
You're driven to;
You can't be soft –
A man like that;
But Oh it seems –
I don't know what –
To hang a man!

The Dice were Loaded

Mary Gilmore

The dice were loaded full and well
The dreadful night that I was born,
The devils danced a tarantelle,
The whimpering plovers fled the corn.

A fox that hunted hungry food
Lifted his head in ravaged cry;
A shadow ran from out the wood,
In after years that shade was I.

I trod the dark mile all alone,
I trod it lone through all the years;
And but the midnight heard my moan,
And but the bitter earth my tears.

I make no plaint, I make no cry,
No back look give to yesterday;
For, where I saw the hazard lie,
I played the game they bid me play.

And now I hang upon a tree,
My lovely body all forlorn;
The loaded dice were thrown for me
Upon the night that I was born.

What's the Difference

Laurence Lerner

The world (one often hears)
Must be full of murderers.
Not all that many are caught;
There are plenty walking about

Sometimes they pull it off
And lead a blameless life,
Good to the wives they wed
By bashing in someone's head

So it's natural to wonder how
They differ from me or you.
Conscience? Consciences are
As calm as they appear.

I can make out in the sea
That washes my memory
Storms as sombre as ever
Darkened to wicked weather.

Hatred so great it might
Press my fingers as tight
On windpipe or on gun
As now around this pen.

If conscience is a sea
It answers from day to day
To what the weather is like.
The rest is only luck.

Did your girl say no
When the storm began to blow?
Was somebody passing when
You happened to raise the gun?

Weather's another name
For imagination;
And if yours is blustery
It imposes on the sea

Billows that rear up higher
Than intention, even desire;
Or a slow enormous swell
That is more than enough to kill.

Outcasts, Rejects
and Misfits

Photograph by Sven Oredson. By courtesy of P.A.F. International.

The Place's Fault

Philip Hobsbaum

Once, after a rotten day at school –
Sweat on my fingers, pages thumbed with smears,
Cane smashing down to make me keep them neat –
I blinked out to the sunlight and the heat
And stumbled up the hill, still swallowing tears.
A stone hissed past my ear – 'yah! gurt fat fool!'

Some urchins waited for me by my gate.
I shouted swear-words at them, walked away.
'Yeller,' they yelled, 'e's yeller!' And they flung
Clods, stones, bricks – anything to make me run.
I ran, all right, up hill all scorching day
With 'yeller' in my ears. 'I'm not, I'm not!'

Another time, playing too near the shops –
Oddly no doubt, I'm told I was quite odd,
Making, no doubt, a noise – a girl in slacks
Came out and told some kids 'Run round the back,
Bash in his back door, smash up his back yard,
And if he yells I'll go and fetch the cops.'

And what a rush I had to lock those doors
Before the rabble reached them! What desire
I've had these twenty years to lock away
That place where fingers pointed out my play,
Where even the grass was tangled with barbed wire,
Where through the streets I waged continual wars!

We left (it was a temporary halt)
The knots of ragged kids, the wired-off beach,
Faces behind the blinds. I'll not return;
There's nothing there I haven't had to learn,
And I've learned nothing that I'd care to teach –
Except that I know it was the place's fault.

My Parents kept me from Children who were Rough

Stephen Spender

My parents kept me from children who were rough
And who threw words like stones and who wore torn clothes.
Their thighs showed through rags. They ran in the street
And climbed cliffs and stripped by the country streams.

I feared more than tigers their muscles like iron
And their jerking hands and their knees tight on my arms.
I feared the salt coarse pointing of those boys
Who copied my lisp behind me on the road.

They were lithe, they sprang out behind hedges
Like dogs to bark at our world. They threw mud
And I looked another way, pretending to smile.
I longed to forgive them, yet they never smiled.

Red Balloon

Dannie Abse

It sailed across the startled town,
over chapels, over chimney-pots,
wind-blown above a block of flats
before it floated down.

Oddly, it landed where I stood,
and finding's keeping, as you know.
I breathed on it, I polished it,
till it shone like living blood.

It was my shame, it was my joy,
it brought me notoriety.
From all of Wales the rude boys came,
it ceased to be a toy.

I heard the girls of Cardiff sigh
when my balloon, my red balloon,
soared higher like a happiness
towards the dark blue sky.

Nine months since, have I boasted of
my unique, my only precious;
but to no one dare I show it now
however long they swear their love.

'It's a Jew's balloon,' my best friend cried,
'stained with our dear Lord's blood.'
'That I'm a Jew is true,' I said,
said I, 'that cannot be denied.'

'What relevance?' I asked surprised,
'what's religion to do with this?'
'Your red balloon's a Jew's balloon,
let's get it circumcized.'

Then some boys laughed and some boys cursed,
some unsheathed their dirty knives:
some lunged, some clawed at my balloon,
but still it would not burst.

They bled my nose, they cut my eye,
half conscious in the street I heard,
'Give up, give up your red balloon.'
I don't know exactly why.

Father, bolt the door, turn the key,
lest those sad, brash boys return
to insult my faith and steal
my red balloon from me.

The Boy Who lives down our Street

Barrie Law (aged 13)

I know a boy who lives down our street,
He has got defective feet.
He's always looking sad
Which always makes me mad.
He's never happy, he's never gay,
He hardly ever comes out to play.
When he does the kids all bully him because he cannot run,
And this they think spoils their fun.
They take away his crutches and make him fall to the floor,
And if he doesn't get up they bully him all the more.

Strangers

R. S. Thomas

We don't like your white cottage.
We don't like the way you live.
Their sins are venial, the folk
With green blouses you displace.
They have gone proudly away,
Leaving only the dry bed
Of footsteps where there was grass,
Or memory of a face
Forever setting within the glass
Of windows about the door.

You have not been here before.
You will offend with your speech
Winds that preferred hands
Wrung with despair, profound
Audiences of the dead.

The Hunchback in the Park

Dylan Thomas

The hunchback in the park,
A solitary mister
Propped between trees and water
From the opening of the garden lock
That lets the trees and water enter
Until the Sunday sombre bell at dark

Eating bread from a newspaper
Drinking water from the chained cup
That the children filled with gravel
In the fountain basin where I sailed my ship
Slept at night in a dog kennel
But nobody chained him up.

Like the park birds he came early
Like the water he sat down
And Mister they called Hey Mister
The truant boys from the town
Running when he had heard them clearly
On out of sound

Past lake and rockery
Laughing when he shook his paper
Hunchbacked in mockery
Through the loud zoo of the willow groves
Dodging the park keeper
With his stick that picked up leaves.

And the old dog sleeper
Alone between nurses and swans
While the boys among willows
Made the tigers jump out of their eyes
To roar on the rockery stones
And the groves were blue with sailors

Made all day until bell time
A woman figure without fault
Straight as a young elm
Straight and tall from his crooked bones
That she might stand in the night
After the locks and chains

All night in the unmade park
After the railings and shrubberies
The birds the grass the trees the lake
And the wild boys innocent as strawberries
Had followed the hunchback
To his kennel in the dark.

Counting the Mad

Donald Justice

This one was put in a jacket,
This one was sent home,
This one was given bread and meat
But would eat none,
And this one cried No No No No
All day long.

This one looked at the window
As though it were a wall,
This one saw things that were not there,
This one things that were,
And this one cried No No No No
All day long.

This one thought himself a bird,
This one a dog,
And this one thought himself a man,
An ordinary man,
And cried and cried No No No No
All day long.

When I walk in the Market Square

Jemal Isfendiyar (aged 15)

When I walk in the market square,
People's faces turn and stare.
Their eyes sometimes frighten me,
They frighten me because their eyes go through me.

When I walk around a bend,
I clench my fists because it might happen,
They might pounce on me, the white boys,
White boys don't like coloureds,
I don't like them.

Soon as I get home from the market,
My mother asks what did you do there.
I just say oh nothing Ma.
If whites don't touch me,
I won't touch them.

Come away, my Love

Joseph Kariuki (Kenya)

Come away, my love, from streets
Where unkind eyes divide,
And shop windows reflect our difference.
In the shelter of my faithful room rest.

There, safe from opinions, being behind
Myself, I can see only you;
And in my dark eyes your grey
Will dissolve.
　　　　　　　The candlelight throws
Two dark shadows on the wall
Which merge into one as I close beside you.

When at last the lights are out,
And I feel your hand in mine,
Two human breaths join in one,
And the piano weaves
Its unchallenged harmony.

The White Blackbird

Andrew Young

Gulls that in meadows stand,
The sea their native land,
Are not so white as you
Flitting from bough to bough,
You who are white as sin
To your black kith and kin.

Tramp

R. S. Thomas

A knock at the door
And he stands there,
A tramp with his can
Asking for tea,
Strong for a poor man
On his way — where?

He looks at his feet,
I look at the sky;
Over us the planes build
The shifting rafters
Of that new world
We have sworn by.

I sleep in my bed,
He sleeps in the old,
Dead leaves of a ditch.
My dreams are haunted;
Are his dreams rich?
If I wake early,
He wakes cold.

On the Swag

R. A. K. Mason

His body doubled
   under the pack
   that sprawls untidily
   on his old back
   the cold wet deadbeat
   plods up the track

The cook peers out:
   'oh curse that old lag
   here again
   with his clumsy swag
   made of a dirty old
   turnip-bag'

'Bring him in cook
   from the grey level sleet
   put silk on his body
   slippers on his feet,
   give him fire
   and bread and meat

Let the fruit be plucked
   and the cake be iced,
   the bed be snug
   and the wine be spiced
   in the old cove's nightcap:
   for this is Christ.'

In the Catalogue

D. J. Enright

It was a foreign horror.
A cold and lonely hour,
A place waste and littered,
And this figure standing there.

Like at first a prized
Cherry sapling swathed in straw.
It was no tree. It was enclosed
In a straw cocoon, and

Wore a hood of sacking
Over the might-be head
And the should-be shoulders.
It seemed to be looking.

What did I fear the most?
To ignore and bustle past?
To acknowledge and perhaps
Find out what best was lost?

It didn't accost. I did.
Rattling in my outstretched hand,
I hoped that money would talk,
A language of the land.

Some inner motion stirred the straw.
My stomach turned, I waited
For its – what? – its rustling claw
Or something I could not conceive.

What happened was the worst.
Nothing. Or simply, the straw
Subsided. 'Please, please!'
I begged. But nothing more.

Fear is glad to turn to anger.
I threw the money down and left,
Heedless of any danger,
Aside from vomiting.

From twenty yards I turned
To look. The shape stood still.
Another ten yards, and I strained
My eyes on icy shadows –

The shape was scrabbling for my coins!
I thanked my stomach. Then
Thanked God, who'd left the thing
Enough to make a man.

Tramps on Waterloo Station

Robert Morgan

It is 2 a.m. and I wait for a train out of London.
There is nothing to do but sit and wait
On the cold, darkened platform under clocks.
Newspaper vans unload news of governments,
Of science and of sex. There are men around me
Pretending to be travellers, passing time
Expertly in shadows and corners.
Some sleep with oblique heads on chests,
Others embrace warm coffee machines
And stare and wait and ache with silence.
A man talks to himself quietly, facing
A wall and pointing at someone invisible.
As he moves from darkness to sanity he lifts
Up his head and sings an Irish song.
The notes unburden his eyeshut face
And a curved smile links him to a precious
Moment from the past. A man in rags
Lies in a heap on a bench in a bookshop shadow.
He uncurls himself like a tropical plant and
His face is a dark map of his life . . . confused,
Bitter, grimed, diseased, obsolete . . .
My clean, modern clothes and full stomach
Remind me of my sanity and involvement with life.
But we are all moving towards the freedom
Of nonentity and they are the nearest to it.

Gipsies

John Clare

The snow falls deep; the forest lies alone;
The boy goes hasty for his load of brakes,
Then thinks upon the fire and hurries back;
The gipsy knocks his hands and tucks them up,
And seeks his squalid camp, half hid in snow,
Beneath the oak which breaks away the wind,
And bushes close in snow like hovel warm;
There tainted mutton wastes upon the coals,
And the half-wasted dog squats close and rubs,
Then feels the heat too strong, and goes aloof;
He watches well, but none a bit can spare,
And vainly waits the morsel thrown away.
'Tis thus they live – a picture to the place,
A quiet, pilfering, unprotected race.

Lines written on the A20 Arterial Road

John Pudney

The gypsies and their seven rough horses
Are back by London's boundary, between
The filling station and the traffic lights
Where grass on the verges still grows sweet and green.

They bring new clothes-pegs, but also magic
To the houses and gardens in tidy rows
Where everything is known and allowed for,
Where, sweet and green, the packeted lawn seed grows,

Where patent clothes-pegs are bought from Woolworths,
Where television brings the evening grace,
Where the sign about London's boundary
Even among bright hoardings takes pride of place.

Here the soap-soft hands are read by palmists.
Here good or evil fortune at the gate,
With clothes-pegs, dangerously beckoning,
Trades the terrible traffic of luck and fate.

Here naughty children are warned of kidnap,
Changelings disguised by artful hedgerow stains,
Carried off, rustled through shady counties
By means of seven rough horses, never trains;

Comforted not by electricity,
But charcoal fires and water from a pond,
Laughing darkly at every motorist
Between the suburbs and the back of beyond.

Close your eyes and cross a palm with silver.
Close your doors and keep your children still.
In spite of Woolworths, buy some clothes-pegs.
For magic has crept down from over the hill.

From beyond the distant filling station,
The far traffic lights, the last bus stop,
The gypsies and their seven rough horses
Have come, for magic, and sweet green grass to crop.

On their way to town the hedgehog-eaters,
Coming from nowhere, idle and wild,
Peddle wooden clothes-pegs and awaken
In every heart the pangs of a naughty child.

The Refugees

Herbert Read

Mute figures with bowed heads
they travel along the road:
old women, incredibly old
and a hand-cart of chattels.

They do not weep:
their eyes are too raw for tears.

Past them have hastened
processions of retreating gunteams
baggage-wagons and swift horsemen.
Now they struggle along
with the rearguard of a broken army.

We shall hold the enemy towards nightfall
and they will move
mutely into the dark behind us,
only the creaking cart
disturbing their sorrowful serenity.

Say this city has ten million souls

W. H. Auden

Say this city has ten million souls,
Some are living in mansions, some are living in holes:
Yet there's no place for us, my dear, yet there's no place for us.

Once we had a country and we thought it fair,
Look in the atlas and you'll find it there:
We cannot go there now, my dear, we cannot go there now.

In the village churchyard there grows an old yew,
Every spring it blossoms anew:
Old passports can't do that, my dear, old passports can't do that.

The consul banged the table and said;
'If you've got no passport you're officially dead':
But we are still alive, my dear, but we are still alive.

Went to a committee; they offered me a chair;
Asked me politely to return next year:
But where shall we go today, my dear, but where shall we go
    today?

Came to a public meeting; the speaker got up and said:
'If we let them in, they will steal our bread';
He was talking of you and me, my dear, he was talking of you
    and me.

Thought I heard the thunder rumbling in the sky;
It was Hitler over Europe, saying: 'They must die';
O we were in his mind, my dear, O we were in his mind.

Saw a poodle in a jacket fastened with a pin,
Saw a door opened and a cat let in:
But they weren't German Jews, my dear, but they weren't
    German Jews.

Went down the harbour and stood upon the quay,
Saw the fish swimming as if they were free:
Only ten feet away, my dear, only ten feet away.

Walked through a wood, saw the birds in the trees;
They had no politicians and sang at their ease:
They weren't the human race, my dear, they weren't the human
    race.

Dreamed I saw a building with a thousand floors,
A thousand windows and a thousand doors;
Not one of them was ours, my dear, not one of them was ours.

Stood on a great plain in the falling snow;
Ten thousand soldiers marched to and fro:
Looking for you and me, my dear, looking for you and me.

The Boarder

Louis Simpson

The time is after dinner. Cigarettes
        Glow on the lawn;
Glasses begin to tinkle; TV sets
        Have been turned on.

The moon is brimming like a glass of beer
      Above the town,
And love keeps her appointment – 'Harry's here!'
      'I'll be right down.'

But the pale stranger in the furnished room
      Lies on his back
Looking at paper roses, how they bloom,
      And ceilings crack.

In this City

Alan Brownjohn

In this city, perhaps a street.
In this street, perhaps a house.
In this house, perhaps a room
And in this room a woman sitting,
Sitting in the darkness, sitting and crying
For someone who has just gone through the door
And who has just switched off the light
Forgetting she was there.

Mr Bleaney

Philip Larkin

'This was Mr Bleaney's room. He stayed
The whole time he was at the Bodies, till
They moved him.' Flowered curtains, thin and frayed,
Fell to within five inches of the sill,

Whose window shows a strip of building land,
Tussocky, littered. 'Mr Bleaney took
My bit of garden properly in hand.'
Bed, upright chair, sixty-watt bulb, no hook

Behind the door, no room for books or bags –
'I'll take it.' So it happens that I lie
Where Mr Bleaney lay, and stub my fags
On the same saucer-souvenir, and try

Stuffing my ears with cotton-wool, to drown
The jabbering set he egged her on to buy.
I know his habits — what time he came down,
His preference for sauce to gravy, why

He kept on plugging at the four aways —
Likewise their yearly frame: the Frinton folk
Who put him up for summer holidays,
And Christmas at his sister's house in Stoke.

But if he stood and watched the frigid wind
Tousling the clouds, lay on the fusty bed
Telling himself that this was home, and grinned,
And shivered, without shaking off the dread

That how we live measures our own nature,
And at his age having no more to show
Than one hired box should make him pretty sure
He warranted no better, I don't know.

Mr Weary's Room

D. J. Enright

To be a doer, it seems,
Is merely to do harm.

Feed a cast-off kitten —
Another cat to kill my birds.

Save my worms from birds —
And starve my pretty starlings.

Boys break my boughs, they also
Fall from boughs and break their necks.

As well without my help
As with my help.

I once lived in a castle. Oh
So many doors, dear me, and windows!

(Who built the castle? That
Was long before my tenancy.)

So tiring! Every vista noted
A fresh wrong to be righted . . .

But now a strict monogamy,
One room, one door, one window –

And still too large a view.
Crawl into my cupboard shall I?

Let me tell you a little Story

W. H. Auden

Let me tell you a little story
   About Miss Edith Gee;
She lived in Clevedon Terrace
   At Number 83

She'd a slight squint in her left eye,
   Her lips they were thin and small,
She had narrow sloping shoulders
   And she had no bust at all.

She'd a velvet hat with trimmings,
   And a dark grey serge costume;
She lived in Clevedon Terrace
   In a small bed-sitting room.

She'd a purple mac for wet days.
   A green umbrella too to take,
She'd a bicycle with shopping basket
   And a harsh back-pedal brake.

The Church of Saint Aloysius
   Was not so very far;
She did a lot of knitting,
   Knitting for that Church Bazaar.

Miss Gee looked up at the starlight
   And said: 'Does anyone care
That I live in Clevedon Terrace
   On one hundred pounds a year?'

She dreamed a dream one evening
    That she was the Queen of France
And the Vicar of Saint Aloysius
    Asked Her Majesty to dance.

But a storm blew down the palace,
    She was biking through a field of corn,
And a bull with the face of the Vicar
    Was charging with lowered horn.

She could feel his hot breath behind her,
    He was going to overtake;
And the bicycle went slower and slower
    Because of that back-pedal brake.

Summer made the trees a picture,
    Winter made them a wreck;
She bicycled to the evening service
    With her clothes buttoned up to her neck.

She passed by the loving couples,
    She turned her head away;
She passed by the loving couples
    And they didn't ask her to stay.

Miss Gee sat down in the side-aisle,
    She heard the organ play;
And the choir it sang so sweetly
    At the ending of the day,

Miss Gee knelt down in the side-aisle,
    She knelt down on her knees;
'Lead me not into temptation
    But make me a good girl, please.'

The days and nights went by her
    Like waves round a Cornish wreck;
She bicycled down to the doctor
    With her clothes buttoned up to her neck.

She bicycled down to the doctor,
    And rang the surgery bell;
'O, doctor, I've a pain inside me,
    And I don't feel very well.'

Doctor Thomas looked her over,
    And then he looked some more;
Walked over to his wash-basin,
    Said, 'Why didn't you come before?'

Doctor Thomas sat over his dinner,
    Though his wife was waiting to ring;
Rolled his bread into pellets,
    Said, 'Cancer's a funny thing.

'Nobody knows what the cause is,
    Though some pretend they do;
It's like some hidden assassin
    Waiting to strike at you.

'Childless women get it,
    And men when they retire;
It's as if there had to be some outlet
    For their foiled creative fire.'

His wife she rang for the servant,
    Said, 'Don't be so morbid, dear',
He said: 'I saw Miss Gee this evening
    And she's a goner, I fear.'

They took Miss Gee to the hospital,
    She lay there a total wreck,
Lay in the ward for women
    With the bedclothes right up to her neck.

They laid her on the table,
    The students began to laugh;
And Mr Rose the surgeon
    He cut Miss Gee in half.

Mr Rose he turned to his students,
    Said, 'Gentlemen, if you please,
We seldom see a sarcoma
    As far advanced as this.'

They took her off the table,
    They wheeled away Miss Gee
Down to another department
    Where they study Anatomy.

They hung her from the ceiling,
    Yes, they hung up Miss Gee;
And a couple of Oxford Groupers
    Carefully dissected her knee.

Found on a Building Site

Martin Seymour-Smith

'Dear One:
    I am naked on a building site
In Penge West. It is 1.5 a.m., and cold;
The mist wreathes around me, rising in columns.
I shall have much to think of, but chiefly
What shall I do at dawn?
I am writing this with a piece of coal
On a sheet of a tramp's stained newspaper. . . .
Dum spiro spero: perhaps you will find this
Before the gaunt sirens of daybreak speak.
If not, then think of me, but make no enquiries.'

Thus sometimes the poor spirit.

Not Waving but Drowning

Stevie Smith

Nobody heard him, the dead man,
But still he lay moaning:
I was much further out than you thought
And not waving but drowning.

Poor chap, he always loved larking
And now he's dead
It must have been too cold for him his heart gave way,
They said.

Oh, no no no, it was too cold always
(Still the dead one lay moaning)
I was much too far out all my life
And not waving but drowning.

Suicides

J. C. Hall

Reading the evening papers we meet them,
Those anonymous names:
She who turned the gas on her sorrow,
He whom the Thames
Left one night more derelict on its shore
Than a child at the convent door.

Little we knew them, these who in their lives
Rated no column.
And even now only between the lines
May we glimpse the solemn
Dilemmas that drove them thither, and guess
Something of their last loneliness.

What of this girl? Surely her beauty might
Have confounded the shades?
Or was it beauty itself that led her
Into the glades
Of darkness where, by love's fever oppressed,
She sought to be dispossessed?

And what of him they found in the chilly dawn
With the tide in his hair?
They say in drowning a man unravels all
His history there
In a fleeting moment, before he falls away
On eternal silence. So he may

Have found at last in some long-sought, half-forgotten
Memory a mirror
Reflecting his first true self, distorted since
By childhood terror.
Oh then perhaps — the pattern revealed — too late
He saw his meaningless fate . . .

We cannot know. For even the notes they left
In their desolate rooms
Can tell us little but that our restless souls
To unknown dooms
Move on; while still, deep in each human face,
We seek the signature of grace.

Tragic their deaths, more tragic the aching thought
That had we been there
We might have laid our hands on their hands and cried
'Do not despair!
For here, even here in this living touch, this breath,
May be the secret you seek in death.'

Conforming and Protesting

Photograph by Adam Ritchie.

Last Lesson of the Afternoon

D. H. Lawrence

When will the bell ring, and end this weariness?
How long have they tugged the leash, and strained apart,
My pack of unruly hounds! I cannot start
Them again on a quarry of knowledge they hate to hunt,
I can haul them and urge them no more.

No longer now can I endure the brunt
Of the books that lie out on the desks; a full threescore
Of several insults of blotted pages, and scrawl
Of slovenly work that they have offered me.
I am sick, and what on earth is the good of it all?
What good to them or me, I cannot see!

       So, shall I take
My last dear fuel of life to heap on my soul
And kindle my will to a flame that shall consume
Their dross of indifference; and take the toll
Of their insults in punishment? — I will not! —

I will not waste my soul and my strength for this.
What do I care for all that they do amiss!
What is the point of this teaching of mine, and of this
Learning of theirs? It all goes down the same abyss.

What does it matter to me, if they can write
A description of a dog, or if they can't?
What is the point? To us both, it is all my aunt!
And yet I'm supposed to care, with all my might.

I do not, and will not; they won't and they don't; and that's all!
I shall keep my strength for myself; they can keep theirs as well.
Why should we beat our heads against the wall
Of each other? I shall sit and wait for the bell.

Maladjusted Boys

Robert Morgan

I have made ten minutes of silence.
I know they are afraid of silence
And the mind's pattern of order.
They gaze at me out of oblique faces
And try to fidget away the bleak thoughts
Simmering in the dark tangle of their minds.
I read their unfriendly eyes, cushion
The confused hatred, stand presumptuously
And pretend not to be afraid.
I keep at them with my eyes,
Will them to work and ride
The storm in a roomful of cold attention.
Here and there faces cringe
And I read a future . . . the dark corner
Of a street hiding the cruel
Thud of a chain or boot.
I see a hunter mask glow on a face
And grimy nailbitten hands bend a ruler
To its limit . . . all this in a room
Yellow with June sun and music
Of birds from a private wood.

Last Lesson of the Afternoon

Susan Ford (aged 14)

Who wants to work
On a sunny afternoon?
I'm not working,
The bell will go soon.

A voice from the depths roars,
'How many have you done?'
My quiet voice
Answers back, 'None.'

The Row

Linda Whitehead (aged 14)

(a daughter to her mother)

I've explained it all to her,
But she still can't see sense.
So I explain it again
And again
And again.
She still says I'm wrong
– Raises her voice a little.
I raise mine louder
And louder
And louder.
She says things.
I say things too,
Then rush off in a huff,
Sorry there had to be a row
But not sorry for what I'd said.

The Collar

George Herbert

I struck the board, and cried, No more.
                    I will abroad.
What? shall I ever sigh and pine?
My lines and life are free; free as the road,
    Loose as the wind, as large as store.
            Shall I be still in suit?
Have I no harvest but a thorn
To let me blood, and not restore
What I have lost with cordial fruit?
                    Sure there was wine
Before my sighs did dry it: there was corn
            Before my tears did drown it.
Is the year only lost to me?
            Have I no bays to crown it?
No flowers, no garlands gay? all blasted?
                    All wasted?
Not so, my heart: but there is fruit,
                    And thou hast hands.
Recover all thy sigh-blown age

On double pleasures: leave thy cold dispute
Of what is fit, and not; forsake thy cage,
   Thy rope of sands,
Which petty thoughts have made, and made to thee
 Good cable, to enforce and draw,
   And be thy law,
While thou didst wink and wouldst not see.
   Away; take heed:
   I will abroad.
Call in thy death's head there: tie up thy fears.
   He that forbears
 To suit and serve his need
   Deserves his load.
But as I raved and grew more fierce and wild
   At every word,
Me thoughts I heard one calling, *Child*:
 And I replied, *My Lord*.

The Man in the Bowler Hat

A. S. J. Tessimond

I am the unnoticed, the unnoticeable man:
The man who sat on your right in the morning train:
The man you looked through like a windowpane:
The man who was the colour of the carriage, the colour of the
 mounting
Morning pipe smoke.

I am the man too busy with living to live,
Too hurried and worried to see and smell and touch:
The man who is patient too long and obeys too much
And wishes too softly and seldom.

I am the man they call the nation's backbone,
Who am boneless — playable catgut, pliable clay:
The Man they label Little lest one day
I dare to grow.

I am the rails on which the moment passes,
The megaphone for many words and voices:
I am graph, diagram,
Composite face.

I am the led, the easily-fed,
The tool, the not-quite-fool,
The would-be-safe-and-sound,
The uncomplaining bound,
The dust fine-ground,
Stone-for-a-statue waveworn pebble-round.

Train to Work

Bernard Spencer

9.20; the Underground groans him to his work;
he sits fumbling a letter; is that
a cheque attached? He is puzzled, frowns
sadly like Rhesus monkeys, like us. Above
the frown fair hair is thinning. Specially
I celebrate his toes turned in, his worn
shoes splashed with mud (but his hands
are clean and fine), the bottoms of his striped trousers
crumpled by rain.
                            In a little while his station
will syphon him out with the others, along, round, away
as a drop goes with its Niagara.
                                            And because
he bears the cracking brunt of things he has never willed
and has eight mean hours a day
to live at the bidding of the gods, and is gentle and put upon
this blindfold bull-fight nag, endearing stranger,
and before long, like others who come to mind,
is condemned to sure death, he sits
(with his mackintosh belt twisted),
poetry roaring from him like a furnace.

For the Record

George Jonas

I think that I live in a street
Where the evenings are decidedly darker,
A citizen of what is said to be a country,
In the year nineteen-sixty-four.

All the snow melts around April,
In August there is nothing to wait for,
The Fall is established in November,
January is mostly Winter.

A woman claims to be my wife
On the strength of which she lives in my house.
But I am also dangerous to some animals
And have at times been observed to eat them.

I have little to say about the structure of society,
There may be certain letters to write occasionally,
Certain amounts to pay when they become due,
But it is against the law for some people to hurt me.

In view of this I continue to lead
What I am told is an existence
Weeks ending in Sundays
Unasked questions scrupulously unanswered.

Security

Michael Hamburger

1

So he's got there at last, been received as a partner –
In a firm going bankrupt;
Found the right place (walled garden), arranged for a mortgage –
But they're pulling the house down
To make room for traffic.

Worse winds are rising. He takes out new policies
For his furniture, for his life,
At a higher premium
Against more limited risks.

Who can face the winds, till the panes crack in their frames?
And if a man faced them, what in the end could he do
But look for shelter like all the rest?
The winds too are afraid, and blow from fear.

I hear my children at play
And recall that one branch of the elm-tree looks dead;
Also that twenty years ago now I could have been parchment
Cured and stretched for a lampshade,
Who now have children, a lampshade
And the fear of those winds.

I saw off the elm-tree branch
To find that the wood was sound;
Mend the fences yet again,
Knowing they'll keep out no one,
Let alone the winds.
For still my children play,
And shall tomorrow, if the weather holds.

Noah

Roy Daniels

They gathered around and told him not to do it,
They formed a committee and tried to take control,
They cancelled his building permit and they stole
His plans. I sometimes wonder he got through it.
He told them wrath was coming, they would rue it,
He begged them to believe the tides would roll,
He offered them passage to his destined goal,
A new world. They were finished and he knew it.
All to no end.
        And then the rain began.
A spatter at first that barely wet the soil,
Then showers, quick rivulets lacing the town,
Then deluge universal. The old man
Arthritic from his years of scorn and toil
Leaned from the admiral's walk and watched them drown.

Cage

Bernard Spencer

That canary measures out its prison.
To perch as quick as camera-shutter, perch
Is left for the little hoop where it can swing.
The next thing is the wiry wall, and cling
With tail and twiggy feet. Then back to perch.
Then it fluffs out its throat and sings, content,
As I can judge, born barred.
There follows its tour of the globe, watch till you tire;
Perch, hoop, and wire,
Perch, wire, and hoop.
A minute shows its life, but I watch hard,
Fascinated, who have to write
An account of myself in five hundred words
For a sociological group.
Neat fists of wire clench around caged birds;
Human cages narrow or retreat.
The dead laws of a stiffening State
Shoot up forests of oppressive iron;
The shouting of each military saviour
Bolts bars of iron;
Money, houses, shudder into iron.
Within that fence I am whatever I am.
And I carry my inherited wish to be free,
And my inherited wish to be tied for ever,
As natural to me as my body.
Unlike the bird in the cage, feather to wire,
I lean out some hours,
I lunge to left, I lunge out to right
And hit no bars that way, only mist's pretence;
I cannot estimate my powers.
But, measuring man and bird,
In this respect the likeness stays:
Much of my life will go to exploring my fence.

The Fable of the Trained White Horses

Jiri Filip

The trained white horses,
surely you know them from the circus
on command they show their teeth
or break into a gallop.

If the trainer cracks his whip
they gallop as he wants, even backwards,
each horse in a row of horses' bodies
with the nostrils of its partner at its tail,

And as thus trot the trained white horses
they nod their heads in unison,
and neigh — that's important,
not what they think in secret.

The trainer cracks the whip again, and look,
one trained white show-horse
dilates his nostrils rapturously,
rears up suddenly on his hind legs.

The others paw the ground and swirl the dust,
then gallop again and neigh,
until the man with the whip, their god,
drives them back to their stable.

Moral
This most successful drill
would not be so successful
if these trained white horses
were not frightened — and their mangers were not full.

The State

Randall Jarrell

When they killed my mother it made me nervous;
I thought to myself, It was *right*:
Of course she was crazy, and how she ate!
And she died, after all, in her way, for the State.
But I minded: how queer it was to stare
At one of them not sitting there.

When they drafted Sister I said all night,
'It's healthier there in the fields';
And I'd think, 'Now I'm helping to win the War,'
When the neighbours came in, as they did, with my meals.
And I was, I was; but I was scared
With only one of them sitting there.

When they took my cat for the Army Corps
Of Conservation and Supply,
I thought of him there in the cold with the mice
And I cried, and I cried, and I wanted to die.
They were there, and I saw them, and that is my life.
Now there's nothing. I'm dead, and I want to die.

The Epoch

Mieczyslaw Jastrun

From one window I saw
Garages of the Security Police.
Building for two years
Girded with barbed wire
Guarded by high camp towers –
Prisoners.

Rising at dawn to the whine of sirens,
Unwilling, sleepy,
In grey prisoner's dress,
They built the vault of a steel hall
For mechanical animals.
Sometimes one of them tried to escape.
Then was heard close, close,
The dry crack of rifle shots.

From a second window I saw
Another building grow.
Free builders
Raised a wall,
Unknown:
Wall of a lunatic asylum or the House of the Dead.

You told me:
'If you do as they want,
You will find yourself here.
If you resist,
You will find yourself there.'

The Drum

John Scott (of Amwell)

I hate that drum's discordant sound,
Parading round, and round, and round:
To thoughtless youth it pleasure yields,
And lures from cities and from fields,
To sell their liberty for charms
Of tawdry lace, and glittering arms;
And when Ambition's voice commands,
To march, and fight, and fall, in foreign lands.

I hate that drum's discordant sound,
Parading round, and round, and round:
To me it talks of ravag'd plains,
And burning towns, and ruin'd swains,
And mangled limbs, and dying groans,
And widows' tears, and orphans' moans;
And all that Misery's hand bestows,
To fill the catalogue of human woes.

Song of the Storm Trooper

Bertolt Brecht (translated by H. R. Hays)

From hunger I grew drowsy
Dulled by my belly's ache.
Then someone shouted in my ear:
Germany awake!

Then I saw many marching
Toward the Third Reich, they said.
Since I had nought to lose
I followed where they led.

And as I marched, there marched
Big Belly at my side.
When I shouted 'Bread and jobs',
'Bread and jobs,' he cried.

The leaders wore high boots,
I stumbled with wet feet.
Yet all of us were marching
To the selfsame beat.

I wanted to march leftward,
Squads right, the order was.
I blindly followed orders
For better or for worse.

And toward some new Third Reich,
But scarcely knowing whither,
Pale and hungry men
And well fed marched together.

They gave me a revolver
And said: now shoot our foe!
But as I fired on his ranks
I laid my brother low.

It was my brother, hunger
Made us one I know.
And I am marching, marching
With my own and my brother's foe.

So I have lost my brother,
I wove his winding sheet.
I know now by this victory
I wrought my own defeat.

Bayonet Charge

Ted Hughes

Suddenly he awoke and was running – raw
In raw-seamed hot khaki, his sweat heavy,
Stumbling across a field of clods towards a green hedge
That dazzled with rifle fire, hearing
Bullets smacking the belly out of the air –
He lugged a rifle numb as a smashed arm;
The patriotic tear that had brimmed in his eye
Sweating like molten iron from the centre of his chest –

In bewilderment then he almost stopped –
In what cold clockwork of the stars and the nations
Was he the hand pointing that second? He was running
Like a man who has jumped up in the dark and runs
Listening between his footfalls for the reason
Of his still running, and his foot hung like
Statuary in mid-stride. Then the shot-slashed furrows

Threw up a yellow hare that rolled like a flame
And crawled in a threshing circle, its mouth wide
Open silent, its eyes standing out.
He plunged past with his bayonet toward the green hedge.
King, honour, human dignity, etcetera
Dropped like luxuries in a yelling alarm
To get out of that blue crackling air
His terror's touchy dynamite.

Memorial Tablet

(Great War)

Siegfried Sassoon

Squire nagged and bullied till I went to fight,
(Under Lord Derby's Scheme). I died in hell —
(They called it Passchendaele). My wound was slight,
And I was hobbling back; and then a shell
Burst slick upon the duck-boards: so I fell
Into the bottomless mud, and lost the light.

At sermon-time, while Squire is in his pew,
He gives my gilded name a thoughtful stare;
For, though low down upon the list, I'm there;
'In proud and glorious memory' . . . that's my due.
Two bleeding years I fought in France, for Squire:
I suffered anguish that he's never guessed.
Once I came home on leave: and then went west . . .
What greater glory could a man desire?

Lamentations

Siegfried Sassoon

I found him in the guard-room at the Base.
From the blind darkness I had heard his crying
And blundered in. With puzzled, patient face
A sergeant watched him; it was no good trying
To stop it; for he howled and beat his chest.
And, all because his brother had gone west,
Raved at the bleeding war; his rampant grief
Moaned, shouted, sobbed, and choked, while he was kneeling
Half-naked on the floor. In my belief
Such men have lost all patriotic feeling.

Dulce et Decorum Est

Wilfred Owen

Bent double, like old beggars under sacks,
Knock-kneed, coughing like hags, we cursed through sludge,
Till on the haunting flares we turned our backs
And towards our distant rest began to trudge.
Men marched asleep. Many had lost their boots
But limped on, blood-shod. All went lame; all blind;
Drunk with fatigue; deaf even to the hoots
Of tired, outstripped Five-Nines that dropped behind.

Gas! GAS! Quick, boys! – An ecstasy of fumbling,
Fitting the clumsy helmets just in time;
But someone still was yelling out and stumbling
And floud'ring like a man in fire or lime . . .
Dim, through the misty panes and thick green light,
As under a green sea, I saw him drowning.

In all my dreams, before my helpless sight,
He plunges at me, guttering, choking, drowning.

If in some smothering dreams you too could pace
Behind the wagon that we flung him in,
And watch the white eyes writhing in his face,
His hanging face, like a devil's sick of sin;
If you could hear, at every jolt, the blood
Come gargling from the froth-corrupted lungs,
Obscene as cancer, bitter as the cud
Of vile, incurable sores on innocent tongues –
My friend, you would not tell with such high zest
To children ardent for some desperate glory,
The old lie: Dulce et decorum est
Pro patria mori

Reason for Refusal

Martin Bell

Busy old lady, charitable tray
Of social emblems: poppies, people's blood –
I must refuse, make you flush pink
Perplexed by abrupt No-thank-you.
Yearly I keep up this small priggishness,
Would wince worse if I wore one.
Make me feel better, fetch a white feather, do.

Everyone has list of dead in war,
Regrets most of them, e.g.

Uncle Cyril; small boy in lace and velvet
With pushing sisters muscling all around him,
And lofty brothers, whiskers and stiff collars;
The youngest was the one who copped it.
My mother showed him to me,
Neat letters high up on the cenotaph
That wedding-caked it up above the park,
And shadowed birds on Isaac Watts' white shoulders

And father's friends, like Sandy Vincent;
Brushed sandy hair, moustache, and staring eyes.
Kitchener claimed him, but the Southern Railway
Held back my father, made him guilty.
I hated the khaki photograph,
It left a patch on the wallpaper after I took it down.

Others I knew stick in the mind,
And Tony Lister often –
Eyes like holes in foolscap, suffered from piles,
Day after day went sick with constipation
Until they told him he could drive a truck –
Blown up with Second Troop in Greece:
We sang all night once when we were on guard.

And Ken Gee, our lance-corporal, Christian Scientist –
Everyone liked him, knew that he was good –
Had leg and arm blown off, then died.

Not all were good. Gross Corporal Rowlandson
Fell in the canal, the corrupt Sweet-water,
And rolled there like a log, drunk and drowned.
And I've always been glad of the death of Dick Benjamin,
A foxy urgent dainty ball-room dancer –
Found a new role in military necessity
As R.S.M. He waltzed out on parade
To make himself hated. Really hated, not an act.
He was a proper little porcelain sergeant-major –
The earliest bomb made smithereens:
Coincidence only, several have assured me.

In the school hall was pretty glass
Where prissy light shone through St George –
The highest holiest manhood, he!
And underneath were slain Old Boys
In tasteful lettering on whited slab –
And, each November, Ferdy the Headmaster
Reared himself squat and rolled his eyeballs upward,
Rolled the whole roll-call off an oily tongue,
Remorselessly from A to Z.

Of all the squirmers, Roger Frampton's lips
Most elegantly curled, showed most disgust.
He was a pattern of accomplishments,
And joined the Party first, and left it first,
At OCTU won a prize belt, most improbable,
Was desert-killed in '40, much too soon.

His name should burn right through that monument.

No poppy, thank you.

The Conscientious Objector

Karl Shapiro

The gates clanged and they walked you into jail
More tense than felons but relieved to find
The hostile world shut out, the flags that dripped
From every mother's windowpane, obscene
The bloodlust sweating from the public heart,
The dog authority slavering at your throat.
A sense of quiet, of pulling down the blind
Possessed you. Punishment you felt was clean.

The decks, the catwalks, and the narrow light
Composed a ship. This was a mutinous crew
Troubling the captains for plain decencies,
A *Mayflower* brim with pilgrims headed out
To establish new theocracies to west,
A Noah's ark coasting the topmost seas
Ten miles above the sodomites and fish.
These inmates loved the only living doves.

Like all men hunted from the world you made
A good community, voyaging the storm
To no safe Plymouth or green Ararat;
Trouble or calm, the men with Bibles prayed,
The gaunt politicals construed our hate.
The opposite of all armies, you were best
Opposing uniformity and yourselves;
Prison and personality were your fate.

You suffered not so physically but knew
Maltreatment, hunger, ennui of the mind.
Well might the soldier kissing the hot beach
Erupting in his face damn all your kind.
Yet you who saved neither yourselves nor us
Are equally with those who shed the blood
The heroes of our cause. Your conscience is
What we come back to in the armistice.

Dooley is a Traitor

James Michie

'So then you won't fight?
'Yes, your Honour,' I said, 'that's right.'
'Now is it that you simply aren't willing,
Or have you a fundamental moral objection to killing?'
Says the judge, blowing his nose
And making his words stand to attention in long rows.
I stand to attention too, but with half a grin
(In my time I've done a good many in.)
'No objection at all, sir,' I said.
'There's a deal of the world I'd rather see dead –
Such as Johnny Stubbs or Fred Settle or my last landlord, Mr
    Syme,

Give me a gun and your blessing, your Honour, and I'll be shoot-
  ing them all the time.
But my conscience says a clear no
To killing a crowd of gentlemen I don't know.
Why, I'd as soon think of killing a worshipful judge,
High-court, like yourself (against whom, God knows, I've got
  no grudge —
So far), as murder a heap of foreign folk.
If you've got no grudge, you've got no joke
To laugh at after.'
                              Now the words never come flowing
Proper for me till I get the old pipe going.
And just as I was poking.
Down baccy, the judge looks up sharp with 'No smoking,
Mr Dooley. We're not fighting this war for fun.
And we want a clearer reason why you refuse to carry a
  gun.
This war is not a personal feud, it's a fight
Against wrong ideas on behalf of the Right.
Mr Dooley, won't you help to destroy evil ideas?'
'Ah, your Honour, here's
The tragedy,' I said. 'I'm not a man of the mind.
I couldn't find it in my heart to be unkind
To an idea. I wouldn't know one if I saw one. I haven't one of
  my own.
So I'd best be leaving other people's alone.'
'Indeed,' he sneers at me, 'this defence is
Curious for someone with convictions in two senses.
A criminal invokes conscience to his aid
To support an individual withdrawal from a communal crusade
Sanctioned by God, led by the Church, against a godless, church-
  less nation!'
I asked his Honour for a translation.
'You talk of conscience,' he said. 'What do you know of the
  Christian creed?'
'Nothing, sir, except what I can read.
That's the most you can hope for from us jail-birds.
I just open the Book here and there and look at the words.
And I find when the Lord himself misliked an evil notion
He turned it into a pig and drove it squealing over a cliff into the
  ocean,
And the loony ran away
And lived to think another day.
There was a clean job done and no blood shed!
Everybody happy and forty wicked thoughts drowned dead.
A neat and Christian murder. None of your mad slaughter

Throwing away the brains with the blood and the baby with the
    bathwater.
Now I look at the war as a sportsman. It's a matter of choosing
The decentest way of losing.
Heads or tails, losers or winners,
We all lose, we're all damned sinners.
And I'd rather be with the poor cold people at the wall that's shot
Than the bloody guilty devils in the firing-line, in Hell and keeping
    hot.'
'But what right, Dooley, what right,' he cried,
'Have you to say the Lord is on your side?'
'That's a dirty crooked question,' back I roared.
'I said not the Lord was on my side, but I was on the side of the
    Lord.'
Then he was up at me and shouting,
But by and by he calms: 'Now we're not doubting
Your sincerity, Dooley, only your arguments,
Which don't make sense.'
('Hullo,' I thought, 'that's the wrong way round.
I may be skylarking a bit, but my brainpan's sound.')
Then biting his nail and sugaring his words sweet:
'Keep your head, Mr Dooley. Religion is clearly not up your
    street.
But let me ask you as a plain patriotic fellow
Whether you'd stand there so smug and yellow
If the foe were attacking your own dear sister.'
'I'd knock their brains out, mister,
On the floor,' I said. 'There,' he says kindly, 'I knew you were no
    pacifist.
It's your straight duty as a man to enlist.
The enemy is at the door.' You could have downed
Me with a feather. 'Where?' I gasped, looking round.
'Not this door,' he says angered. 'Don't play the clown.
But they're two thousand miles away planning to do us down.
Why, the news is full of the deeds of those murderers and rapers.'
'Your Eminence,' I said, 'my father told me never to believe the
    papers
But to go by my eyes,
And at two thousand miles the poor things can't tell truth from
    lies.'
His fearful spectacles glittered like the moon: 'For the last time
    what right
Has a man like you to refuse to fight?'
'More right,' I said, 'than you.
You've never murdered a man, so you don't know what it is I
    won't do.

I've done it in good hot blood, so haven't I the right to make bold
To declare that I shan't do it in cold?'
Then the judge rises in a great rage
And writes DOOLEY IS A TRAITOR in black upon a page
And tells me I must die.
'What, me?' says I.
'If you still won't fight.'
'Well, yes, your Honour,' I said, 'that's right.'

Undivided Loyalty

James Kirkup

Nothing is worth dying for.
Some people would rather
Be dead than Red.
But I would simply rather
Not be dead.

I would not die for Britain,
Or any land. Why should I?
I only happened to be born there.
Emigré, banished, why should I defend
A land I never chose, that never wanted me?

I might have been born anywhere –
In mid-Pacific or in Ecuador.
I would not die for the world.
Jesus was wrong.
Only nothing is worth dying for.

No More Hiroshimas

James Kirkup

At the station exit, my bundle in my hand,
Early the afternoon's wet snow
Falls thinly round me, out of a crudded sun.
I had forgotten to remember where I was.
Looking about, I see it might be anywhere –
A station, a town like any other in Japan,
Ramshackle, muddy, noisy, drab; a cheerfully

Shallow permanence: peeling concrete, litter, 'Atomic
Lotion, for hair fall-out,' a flimsy department-store;
Racks and towers of neon, flashy over tiled and tilted waves
Of little roofs, shacks cascading lemons and persimmons,
Oranges and dark-red apples, shanties awash with rainbows
Of squid and octopus, shellfish, slabs of tuna, oysters, ice,
Ablaze with fans of soiled nude-picture books
Thumbed abstractedly by schoolboys, with second-hand looks.

The river remains unchanged, sad, refusing rehabilitation.
In this long, wide, empty official boulevard
The new trees are still small, the office blocks
Basely functional, the bridge a slick abstraction.
But the river remains unchanged, sad, refusing rehabilitation.

In the city centre, far from the station's lively squalor,
A kind of life goes on, in cinemas and hi-fi coffee bars,
In the shuffling racket of pin-table palaces and parlours,
The souvenir-shops piled with junk, kimonoed kewpie-dolls,
Models of the bombed Industry Promotion Hall, memorial ruin
Tricked out with glitter-frost and artificial pearls.

Set in an awful emptiness, the modern tourist hotel is trimmed
With jaded Christmas frippery, flatulent balloons; in the hall,
A giant dingy iced cake in the shape of a Cinderella coach.
The contemporary stairs are treacherous, the corridors
Deserted, my room an overheated morgue, the bar in darkness.
Punctually, the electric chimes ring out across the tidy waste
Their doleful public hymn – the tune unrecognizable, evangelist.

Here atomic peace is geared to meet the tourist trade.
Let it remain like this, for all the world to see,
Without nobility or loveliness, and dogged with shame
That is beyond all hope of indignation. Anger, too, is dead.
And why should memorials of what was far
From pleasant have the grace that helps us to forget?

In the dying afternoon, I wander dying round the Park of Peace.
It is right, this squat, dead place, with its left-over air
Of an abandoned International Trade and Tourist Fair.
The stunted trees are wrapped in straw against the cold.
The gardeners are old, old women in blue bloomers, white aprons,
Survivors weeding the dead brown lawns around the Children's
    Monument.

A hideous pile, the Atomic Bomb Explosion Centre, freezing cold,
'Includes the Peace Tower, a museum containing
Atomic-melted slates and bricks, photos showing
What the Atomic Desert looked like, and other
Relics of the catastrophe.'

The other relics:
The ones that made me weep;
The bits of burnt clothing,
The stopped watches, the torn shirts.
The twisted buttons,
The stained and tattered vests and drawers,
The ripped kimonos and charred boots,
The white blouse polka-dotted with atomic rain, indelible,
The cotton summer pants the blasted boys crawled home in, to
    bleed
And slowly die.

Remember only these.
They are the memorials we need.